BOOK LOVER'S JOURNAL

𝔗𝔥𝔢 𝔑𝔢𝔴 𝔜𝔬𝔯𝔨 𝔗𝔦𝔪𝔢𝔰

Expect the World®

Pomegranate

SAN FRANCISCO

Published by Pomegranate Communications, Inc.

Box 808022, Petaluma CA 94975

800 227 1428; www.pomegranate.com

Pomegranate Europe Ltd.

Unit 1, Heathcote Business Centre, Hurlbutt Road

Warwick, Warwickshire CV34 6TD, UK

[+44] 0 1926 430111

Catalog No. AA308

ISBN 0-7649-3300-0

Designed by Patrice Morris

Printed in Korea

14 13 12 11 10 09 08 07 06 05   10 9 8 7 6 5 4 3 2 1

name: _____

address: _____

_____

_____

telephone: _____

e-mail: _____

_____

_____

EMERGENCY CONTACT INFORMATION

name: _____

address: _____

_____

_____

telephone: _____

e-mail: _____

_____

_____

For more than 150 years, *The New York Times* has brought readers and authors together with its book reviews and coverage of the literary scene. From Charles Dickens to Zadie Smith and from Betty Friedan to Stephen Hawking, *The New York Times* finds, studies, and tells the world about its subtlest thinkers and finest writers.

This journal provides space for you to write your own book reviews. That's a fine way to hone your writing and analytical skills, and in setting down your thoughts about what you've been reading, you may find that you understand it in a new and possibly surprising way.

There is further support for your reading, writing, and thinking projects here: *The New York Times Book Lover's Journal* features pages where you can index your subjects by title and by author; enumerate the books you want to read (to counteract memory failure at the bookstore); and keep track of books you've loaned and borrowed. Quotes from reviews of history-making books along with excerpted articles and headlines from *The New York Times* appear throughout. There's also a section for recording books that have been recommended to you.

It may or may not be true that there is one good book in everyone. But this elegant journaling tool will bring forth plenty of good reviews and help you enjoy your literature habit even more. ❧

Books

I Have
Read

Title: _____

_____

Author: _____

Date completed: _____

Publisher: _____

Notes: _____

_____

_____

_____

_____

_____

_____

_____

_____

_____

_____

_____

Title:

Author:

Date completed:

Publisher:

Notes:

Title: _____

_____

Author: _____

Date completed: _____

Publisher: _____

Notes: _____

_____

_____

_____

_____

_____

_____

_____

_____

_____

_____

_____

Title:

Author:

Date completed:

Publisher:

Notes:

The New York Times

Nov. 23, 1863

NEW BOOKS

Excursions, by Henry David Thoreau, Author of "Walden"
and a "Week on the Concord and Merrimac Rivers." 12mo.
Ticknor & Fields, Boston

More by the breath of friendly opinion and applause,
perhaps, than by his own writings, Thoreau is now
widely known as the man who dared to "live his life"
his own way, irrespective of any other law, a scorner
of shams, the apostle of individuality in an age of
association and compromise, a passionate lover and
practicer of his theory, and consequently somewhat
stern and severe in his isolation, but richly endowed
with traits that endeared him to the few he admitted
to intimacy. That which even the slightest tinge of
affectation would make ridiculous, in Thoreau
became noble and noteworthy, from the singleness of
his aim and the directness with which he pursued it.
Civilized man to him was nothing. Nature, all in all.

Title:

Author:

Date completed:

Publisher:

Notes:

Title:

Author:

Date completed:

Publisher:

Notes:

Title: _____

Author: _____

Date completed: _____

Publisher: _____

Notes: _____

_____

_____

_____

_____

_____

_____

_____

_____

_____

_____

_____

Title: _____

_____

Author: _____

Date completed: _____

Publisher: _____

Notes: _____

_____

_____

_____

_____

_____

_____

_____

_____

_____

_____

_____

_____

_____

Title: _____

Author: _____

Date completed: _____

Publisher: _____

Notes: _____

The New York Times

New-York Daily Times (1851–1857), March 16, 1852

DICKENS—THE REFORMER

The first sheets of "Bleak House,"—Dickens' new novel, have been received in advance of their publication in London, for Harper's Magazine. They have the clear ring of the true metal. . . . The book, it is clear, is to be full of characters, full of incidents, full of humor, pathos and power,—all marshaled with the utmost skill of this great master, to make odious in the sight of heaven and earth, that "most pestilent of hoary sinners," the English High Court of Chancery. It will seek to turn the swelling tide of public contempt, ridicule, indignation and hatred against that great engine of oppression, made sacred by ages of abuse, and venerable in the eyes of all who live only to adore the past. . . . Whether feeble infancy or lusty manhood, stooping age or tender womanhood, is the subject of injustice or perverted institutions, his warm sympathies are always welling over, and his eloquent pen—unequalled in descriptive power—shoots his indignant and withering denunciations throughout the world.

Title:

Author:

Date completed:

Publisher:

Notes:

Title: _____

_____

Author: _____

Date completed: _____

Publisher: _____

Notes: _____

_____

_____

_____

_____

_____

_____

_____

_____

_____

_____

_____

Title: _____

Author: _____

Date completed: _____

Publisher: _____

Notes: _____

_____

_____

_____

_____

_____

_____

_____

_____

_____

_____

_____

_____

_____

_____

_____

Title: _____

Author: _____

Date completed: _____

Publisher: _____

Notes: _____

_____

_____

_____

_____

_____

_____

_____

_____

_____

_____

_____

Title:

Author:

Date completed:

Publisher:

Notes:

The New York Times

Aug. 23, 1869

NEW PUBLICATIONS

The Innocents Abroad, Or The New Pilgrim's Progress, by Mark Twain. (Samuel E. Clemens.) Hartford, Conn.: American Publishing Company

Mark Twain must have made his new *Pilgrim's Progress* in a mood of remarkable thoughtfulness, without any strong amount of tragic feeling; for he is always comic, and always saying facetious things, with no great respect for associations and surroundings—laying wagers on the very top of the Pyramid of Cheops, cracking jokes in the Coliseum, and making the entry into Jerusalem with a hilarity not abated in any perceptible degree. . . . It is altogether a very taking book; and a great many persons who would not care to read the graver accounts of travel through these world-renowned places, will find themselves very much interested in Mark Twain's humorous way of getting over the same ground.

Title:

Author:

Date completed:

Publisher:

Notes:

Title: _____

_____

Author: _____

Date completed: _____

Publisher: _____

Notes: _____

_____

_____

_____

_____

_____

_____

_____

_____

_____

_____

_____

_____

Title:

Author:

Date completed:

Publisher:

Notes:

Title:

Author:

Date completed:

Publisher:

Notes:

Title:

Author:

Date completed:

Publisher:

Notes:

The New York Times

July 6, 1902

WESTERN TOWN HAS LITERARY CENSORS

A new theory of literary censorship has been laid down within the past few days at Evanston, in Illinois, where the local library has made up a sort of "index expurgatorius" or "black list." It is admitted that there are a lot of books in the library which ought to be suppressed, but they are among the classics and so are well known.

It is to new books that the censors particularly devote their attention. As soon as a work of this kind is "suspect" it is read and if found objectionable, as is generally the case, it is hidden away in the attic, so that it will not corrupt the good folk of Evanston.

Title:

Author:

Date completed:

Publisher:

Notes:

Title:

Author:

Date completed:

Publisher:

Notes:

Title:

Author:

Date completed:

Publisher:

Notes:

The New York Times

July 31, 1910

LITTLE STORIES OF FACT AND FANCY

For Summer Reading:

Mother Goose's Rhymes: This collection of elementary gems of English poesy is especially commended for perusal and study by Poet Laureates, who will find the simplified forms here presented conducive to a truer rhythm, deeper meaning, and all around better verse. Mr. Kipling might well dip into these pages before exploding another Burial Ode.

March 15, 1925

MOTHER GOOSE FINDS DEFENDERS AT HAND

Mother Goose today appears to be fighting with her back to the wall for the preservation of an erstwhile impeccable reputation. She is accused of fostering laziness and disrespect in the young, of resorting to the rod instead of to reason, and is accused by Mother Stoner on some sixty other counts. But, despite the contention of a few writers that Mother Goose is not all that she should be, the fact remains that in public school readers used throughout the country there are to be found all the well-known Mother Goose tales. Upward of 9,176,552 children are today reading these stories, or rewritten versions of them, in regular public school curricula.

Title:

Author:

Date completed:

Publisher:

Notes:

Title:

Author:

Date completed:

Publisher:

Notes:

Title:

Author:

Date completed:

Publisher:

Notes:

Title: _____

Author: _____

Date completed: _____

Publisher: _____

Notes: _____

_____

_____

_____

_____

_____

_____

_____

_____

_____

_____

_____

Title:

Author:

Date completed:

Publisher:

Notes:

The New York Times

Aug. 4, 1932

PEARL BUCK, WRITER, IS BACK FROM CHINA

AUTHOR OF "THE GOOD EARTH" SAYS NEWS OF PULITZER AWARD CAME AS SURPRISE TO HER.

Mrs. Pearl S. Buck, who won a host of readers and the Pulitzer Prize for 1932 with her best-selling novel, "The Good Earth," turned momentarily from fiction to fact yesterday after her arrival in New York from China. . . . No thought of winning the Pulitzer Prize had occurred to Mrs. Buck until one morning a cablegram from the United States arrived to interrupt work in her attic. She had believed the Chinese background of her book made her ineligible for the award. She admitted no more writing was done in the attic that day.

Title:

Author:

Date completed:

Publisher:

Notes:

Title: _____

Author: _____

Date completed: _____

Publisher: _____

Notes: _____

_____

_____

_____

_____

_____

_____

_____

_____

_____

_____

_____

_____

_____

Title: _____

_____

Author: _____

Date completed: _____

Publisher: _____

Notes: _____

_____

_____

_____

_____

_____

_____

_____

_____

_____

_____

_____

_____

_____

Title: _____

_____

Author: _____

Date completed: _____

Publisher: _____

Notes: _____

_____

_____

_____

_____

_____

_____

_____

_____

_____

_____

_____

_____

Title: _____

_____

Author: _____

Date completed: _____

Publisher: _____

Notes: _____

_____

_____

_____

_____

_____

_____

_____

_____

_____

_____

_____

_____

The New York Times

Feb. 23, 1933

'OBSCENITY' SCORED IN 3 BEST SELLERS
FATHER TALBOT NOW DIRECTS FIRE AT LEWIS, FAULKNER AND HEMINGWAY.

In a continuation of his magazine and radio attack against allegedly indecent books, the Rev. Francis X. Talbot writes that beneath the "art and literary pretensions" of Sinclair Lewis's "Ann Vickers," and of the novels of William Faulkner and Ernest Hemingway, are "crawling vermin." . . . He differentiates between the "moronic" novels and the books with "literary pretensions," while condemning both. Of the works of Lewis, Faulkner and Hemingway he writes that "these novels are vicious in their depths, while the others are plainly erotic on their surface; these perfume sin and garb it in rainbows, but the others make it bestial and leave it revolting."

Title:

Author:

Date completed:

Publisher:

Notes:

Title: _____

_____

Author: _____

Date completed: _____

Publisher: _____

Notes: _____

_____

_____

_____

_____

_____

_____

_____

_____

_____

_____

_____

 _____

Title:

Author:

Date completed:

Publisher:

Notes:

Title: _____

Author: _____

Date completed: _____

Publisher: _____

Notes: _____

_____

_____

_____

_____

_____

_____

_____

_____

_____

_____

_____

Title:

Author:

Date completed:

Publisher:

Notes:

The New York Times

June 16, 1900

100 BOOKS FOR SUMMER READING

It must also be remembered that no man is so rich as he to whom books are the chief pleasure found in life. With such a taste a man can never be lonely, never completely unhappy, and in all times and places, in crowded towns as in the quiet country, books are never out of place, never without the power to charm, to comfort, to respond to every demand and mood. Without the love of books the richest man may be said to be poor. With it, be he a Thoreau living in a Walden hut, he is rich indeed, in a pleasure that can never decay, never change, and whose resources seem the more endless the more they are drawn upon.

Title:

Author:

Date completed:

Publisher:

Notes:

Title: _____

_____

Author: _____

Date completed: _____

Publisher: _____

Notes: _____

_____

_____

_____

_____

_____

_____

_____

_____

_____

_____

_____

Title:

Author:

Date completed:

Publisher:

Notes:

Title: _____

Author: _____

Date completed: _____

Publisher: _____

Notes: _____

_____

_____

_____

_____

_____

_____

_____

_____

_____

_____

_____

_____

Title: _____

Author: _____

Date completed: _____

Publisher: _____

Notes: _____

_____

_____

_____

_____

_____

_____

_____

_____

_____

_____

_____

The New York Times

Jan. 4, 1948

PEOPLE WHO READ AND WRITE

FOREVER OMAR

A report, garnished with a festoon of ivy and wafted in on the strains of an Alma Mater, comes to us from the Hampshire Bookshop in Northampton, Mass., the seat of Smith College, an institution of higher female learning. The Bookshop—in the course of a survey of student reading tastes—discovered, somewhat to its collective surprise, that its best-selling poet is Omar Khayyam and passes the information along in the interests of peripheral enlightenment. After Omar's "Rubaiyat" come Elizabeth Barrett Browning's "Sonnets from the Portuguese" and Gibran's "The Prophet," and it is not until these bards have twanged their classic and pseudo-classic lyres that the moderns enter the picture of student purchases, with T. S. Eliot and W. H. Auden leading the list. Edna St. Vincent Millay and Sara Teasdale, the favorite poets with students only a few years back, no longer seem to ring much of the poetic bell with today's undergraduates.

Title: _____

Author: _____

Date completed: _____

Publisher: _____

Notes: _____

_____

_____

_____

_____

_____

_____

_____

_____

_____

_____

_____

_____

_____

_____

Title:

Author:

Date completed:

Publisher:

Notes:

Title:

Author:

Date completed:

Publisher:

Notes:

The New York Times

Dec. 31, 1950

IN AND OUT OF BOOKS

By David Dempsey

The most discussed—and unsolved—question of the year was the influence of television on reading. Publishers availed themselves of the new medium to advertise their books, denounced it, pretended to welcome it, discounted its importance. But none ignored it. In the absence of reliable surveys, no one knows to what extent TV had cut into reading time—or increased it. Pessimists along Publishers Row were predicting that reading for entertainment would become as obsolete as pumping a player piano. Optimists were quoting the New York schoolboy who said that the show he had seen on television was so good it almost made him want to read the book.

Title:

Author:

Date completed:

Publisher:

Notes:

Title: _____

Author: _____

Date completed: _____

Publisher: _____

Notes: _____

_____

_____

_____

_____

_____

_____

_____

_____

_____

_____

_____

Books
Recommended
to Me

Title: _____

Author: _____

Publisher: _____

Recommended by: _____

Notes: _____

_____

_____

Title: _____

Author: _____

Publisher: _____

Recommended by: _____

Notes: _____

_____

Title:

Author:

Publisher:

Recommended by:

Notes:

Title:

Author:

Publisher:

Recommended by:

Notes:

The New York Times

Oct. 16, 1961

PAPERBACK BOOKS GAIN STATURE WITH INCREASED USE IN SCHOOLS

By Nan Robertson

The paperback book, described less than a decade ago as a showcase for the "three S's—sex, sadism and the smoking gun"—is doing wonders now with the three R's.

In the last few years it has moved miles up the intellectual ladder. It is being used more and more for education: formal, informal, on all levels and to a fantastic extent.

The paperback revolution is established. What is happening can only be called a paperback explosion, particularly in the field of learning.

Title:

Author:

Publisher:

Recommended by:

Notes:

Title:

Author:

Publisher:

Recommended by:

Notes:

Title:

Author:

Publisher:

Recommended by:

Notes:

Title:

Author:

Publisher:

Recommended by:

Notes:

Title:

Author:

Publisher:

Recommended by:

Notes:

Title:

Author:

Publisher:

Recommended by:

Notes:

Title: _____

_____

Author: _____

Publisher: _____

Recommended by: _____

Notes: _____

_____

_____

_____

Title: _____

_____

Author: _____

Publisher: _____

Recommended by: _____

Notes: _____

_____

_____

Title: _____

Author: _____

Publisher: _____

Recommended by: _____

Notes: _____

_____

_____

_____

Title: _____

Author: _____

Publisher: _____

Recommended by: _____

Notes: _____

_____

_____

The New York Times

Jan. 31, 1886

A FAMOUS RUSSIAN NOVEL

War and Peace: A Historical Novel. Part I. By Count Léon Tolstoi.
Translated into French by a Russian lady, and from the French by
Clara Bell. Revised and corrected in the United States. New York:
Harper & Brothers.

Count Lëo Tolstoi's six-volume historical romance,
"Voina I Mire," (War and Peace), the earlier install-
ments of which were published in Russia as long ago
as 1867, has at length found its way across the Atlantic
under the double disadvantage of having been translated from Russian into French and French into
English. . . . "War and Peace" may be called an illustrated historical essay rather than a novel, there being
no semblance of a plot, and the characters serving to
develop the public events rather than being developed
by them. This inversion of the usual rule, together
with the subtle but unmistakable savor of fatalism
which pervades the whole work, disturbs the reader
with the same sense of vague discomfort that must
have chilled many of Count Tolstoi's foreign admir-
ers when they found their hero living in a shabby,
comfortless, untidy house a little way out of Moscow,
where carpets and clean tablecloths appeared to be
equally rare.

Title:

Author:

Publisher:

Recommended by:

Notes:

Title:

Author:

Publisher:

Recommended by:

Notes:

Title:

Author:

Publisher:

Recommended by:

Notes:

Title:

Author:

Publisher:

Recommended by:

Notes:

Title:

Author:

Publisher:

Recommended by:

Notes:

Title:

Author:

Publisher:

Recommended by:

Notes:

Title:

Author:

Publisher:

Recommended by:

Notes:

Title:

Author:

Publisher:

Recommended by:

Notes:

Title:

Author:

Publisher:

Recommended by:

Notes:

Title:

Author:

Publisher:

Recommended by:

Notes:

The New York Times

Nov. 2, 1962

HENRY MILLER FACES ARREST IN CASE HERE

A warrant for the arrest of Henry Miller was issued in Brooklyn Criminal Court yesterday because of the failure of the author of "Tropic of Cancer" to appear to face an obscenity charge.

Mr. Miller had been charged in a grand jury information with violating a section of the Penal Code covering the writing of obscene literature. Assistant District Attorney Louis Ernst said the charge was based on Mr. Miller's writing of "Tropic of Cancer."

. . . A series of court battles have been held over whether "Tropic of Cancer" is obscene. It was banned from this country from the time it was written in the nineteen-thirties until last year.

Title:

Author:

Publisher:

Recommended by:

Notes:

Title:

Author:

Publisher:

Recommended by:

Notes:

Title: _____

_____

Author: _____

Publisher: _____

Recommended by: _____

Notes: _____

_____

_____

_____

Title: _____

_____

Author: _____

Publisher: _____

Recommended by: _____

Notes: _____

_____

_____

Title:

Author:

Publisher:

Recommended by:

Notes:

Title:

Author:

Publisher:

Recommended by:

Notes:

Title: _____

Author: _____

Publisher: _____

Recommended by: _____

Notes: _____

_____

_____

Title: _____

Author: _____

Publisher: _____

Recommended by: _____

Notes: _____

_____

_____

Title:

Author:

Publisher:

Recommended by:

Notes:

Title:

Author:

Publisher:

Recommended by:

Notes:

The New York Times

Oct. 2, 1891

HERMAN MELVILLE

There has died and been buried in this city, during the current week, at an advanced age, a man who is so little known, even by name, to the generation now in the vigor of life that only one newspaper contained an obituary account of him, and this was but of three or four lines. Yet forty years ago the appearance of a new book by Herman Melville was esteemed a literary event, not only throughout his own country, but so far as the English-speaking race extended.

Title:

Author:

Publisher:

Recommended by:

Notes:

Title:

Author:

Publisher:

Recommended by:

Notes:

Title: _____

_____

Author: _____

Publisher: _____

Recommended by: _____

Notes: _____

_____

_____

_____

Title: _____

_____

Author: _____

Publisher: _____

Recommended by: _____

Notes: _____

_____

_____

Title:

Author:

Publisher:

Recommended by:

Notes:

Title:

Author:

Publisher:

Recommended by:

Notes:

Title:

Author:

Publisher:

Recommended by:

Notes:

Title:

Author:

Publisher:

Recommended by:

Notes:

Title:

Author:

Publisher:

Recommended by:

Notes:

Title:

Author:

Publisher:

Recommended by:

Notes:

The New York Times

Dec. 25, 1932

TWANGS FROM THE LYRES OF PRESIDENTS
MOST OF THE CHIEF EXECUTIVES OF THE NATION HAVE PRODUCED MEMORABLE POETIC LINES, EITHER IN VERSE OR IN PROSE

Critics observe the mounting successes of American poets, the increase of books of verse on the best-seller list and the rising flood of popular anthologies, and they marvel at the "new interest" of Americans in poetry. Yet Americans have always been poetic. . . . If proof be needed, their Presidents prove it. The nation's leaders, chosen because they fairly represented the mind and the spirit of the people of their day, have consistently, though perhaps unconsciously, given voice to the deep fervor of soul that animates American life. . . . The seven poets who became Presidents, or Presidents who became poets, include George Washington, Thomas Jefferson, John Quincy Adams, John Tyler, Abraham Lincoln, James A. Garfield and Grover Cleveland.

To this list may be added ten who wrote prose which is sometimes poetic; John Adams, Andrew Jackson, Rutherford B. Hayes, Benjamin Harrison, William McKinley, Theodore Roosevelt, Woodrow Wilson, Warren G. Harding, Calvin Coolidge and Herbert Hoover. The last three—and indeed several of the earliest ones—cannot be thought of as overwhelmingly poetic in their ways of thinking and expressing themselves. Nevertheless, they had their poetic moments.

Title: _____

Author: _____

Publisher: _____

Recommended by: _____

Notes: _____

_____

_____

_____

_____

_____

Title: _____

_____

Author: _____

Publisher: _____

Recommended by: _____

Notes: _____

_____

_____

_____

Title: _____

_____

Author: _____

Publisher: _____

Recommended by: _____

Notes: _____

_____

_____

Title: _____

_____

Author: _____

Publisher: _____

Recommended by: _____

Notes: _____

_____

_____

Books
Borrowed & Loaned

Title: _____

Author: _____

Borrowed from: _____

Loaned to: _____

Date returned: _____

_____

_____

_____

Title: _____

Author: _____

Borrowed from: _____

Loaned to: _____

Date returned: _____

_____

_____

Title: _____

Author: _____

Borrowed from: _____

Loaned to: _____

Date returned: _____

Title: _____

Author: _____

Borrowed from: _____

Loaned to: _____

Date returned: _____

The New York Times

Aug. 9, 1959

BEST SELLER LIST

Exodus, Uris

Lady Chatterly's Lover, Lawrence

The Ugly American, Lederer and Burdlick

Doctor Zhivago, Pasternak

Dear and Glorious Physician, Caldwell

Celia Garth, Bristow

Lolita, Nabokov

The Light Infantry Ball, Basso

California Street, Busch

Mrs. Arris Goes to Paris, Gallico

Nine Coaches Waiting, Stewart

The Lion, Kessel

The Tents of Wickedness, De Vries

The Young Titan, Mason

The Chinese Box, Eyre

The Art of Llewellyn Jones, Bonner

Title:

Author:

Borrowed from:

Loaned to:

Date returned:

Title:

Author:

Borrowed from:

Loaned to:

Date returned:

Title:

Author:

Borrowed from:

Loaned to:

Date returned:

Title:

Author:

Borrowed from:

Loaned to:

Date returned:

Title: _____

Author: _____

Borrowed from: _____

Loaned to: _____

Date returned: _____

_____

_____

_____

Title: _____

Author: _____

Borrowed from: _____

Loaned to: _____

Date returned: _____

_____

_____

Title: _____

Author: _____

Borrowed from: _____

Loaned to: _____

Date returned: _____

Title: _____

Author: _____

Borrowed from: _____

Loaned to: _____

Date returned: _____

Title: _____

Author: _____

Borrowed from: _____

Loaned to: _____

Date returned: _____

Title: _____

Author: _____

Borrowed from: _____

Loaned to: _____

Date returned: _____

The New York Times

May 12, 1936

LEWIS IS SCORNFUL OF RADIO CULTURE
NOTHING EVER WILL REPLACE THE OLD-FASHIONED BOOK, HE TELLS BOOKSELLERS.

In what he termed his second public address in two years, Sinclair Lewis prophesied last night that no form of radio broadcast, television included, ever would threaten the demand for good books. Mr. Lewis spoke on "Enemies of the Book" at the thirty-sixth annual dinner of the American Booksellers Association, which concluded a two-day convention at the Hotel Pennsylvania. . . . He said he declined to have his talk broadcast, because he wanted merely to "ramble around, unbound by split-second timing, detestable phrase and detestable custom of the radio, where I would be allowed exactly twelve minutes and nine seconds in between the program of the Lollypop Lilters and the Ex-Lax Symphony Orchestra." . . . "It is obvious that people listen to the radio and go to motion pictures instead of reading books, but there are plenty of other Cossacks on our trail, the automobile, the bridge table and night clubs."

Title: _____

Author: _____

Borrowed from: _____

Loaned to: _____

Date returned: _____

Title: _____

Author: _____

Borrowed from: _____

Loaned to: _____

Date returned: _____

Title: _____

Author: _____

Borrowed from: _____

Loaned to: _____

Date returned: _____

_____

_____

_____

Title: _____

Author: _____

Borrowed from: _____

Loaned to: _____

Date returned: _____

_____

_____

Title: _____

Author: _____

Borrowed from: _____

Loaned to: _____

Date returned: _____

_____

_____

_____

_____

Title: _____

Author: _____

Borrowed from: _____

Loaned to: _____

Date returned: _____

Title:

Author:

Borrowed from:

Loaned to:

Date returned:

Title:

Author:

Borrowed from:

Loaned to:

Date returned:

Title: _____

Author: _____

Borrowed from: _____

Loaned to: _____

Date returned: _____

_____

_____

_____

Title: _____

Author: _____

Borrowed from: _____

Loaned to: _____

Date returned: _____

_____

The New York Times

March 1, 1930

ON THE CULTURE FRONT

Humanism in literature is a protest against the violence and the indignities to which the English language has been subjected in the last decade. On the one hand we have had the "staccato" of strong, rough men with hair on their chest. On the other hand are the experiments in widening the "horizons" of the English tongue, leading into the incoherencies of what solemn critics call the cult of unintelligibility and the profane call the "cuckoo press." . . . [T]here are a lot of plain citizens who think that Humanism means that human beings would express themselves in statements like "Two and two are four" or "They that sow in tears shall reap in joy." But when Gertrude Stein says, "The this this of the that that," and James Joyce says, "Eeny meeny homoiousion oh popoi pet and kottle strike me dead," we have broken with human speech and are back in the tree tops.

Title:

Author:

Borrowed from:

Loaned to:

Date returned:

Title:

Author:

Borrowed from:

Loaned to:

Date returned:

Title: _____

Author: _____

Borrowed from: _____

Loaned to: _____

Date returned: _____

_____

_____

_____

Title: _____

Author: _____

Borrowed from: _____

Loaned to: _____

Date returned: _____

_____

_____

Title: _____

Author: _____

Borrowed from: _____

Loaned to: _____

Date returned: _____

Title: _____

Author: _____

Borrowed from: _____

Loaned to: _____

Date returned: _____

Title: _____

Author: _____

Borrowed from: _____

Loaned to: _____

Date returned: _____

Title: _____

Author: _____

Borrowed from: _____

Loaned to: _____

Date returned: _____

Title: _____

Author: _____

Borrowed from: _____

Loaned to: _____

Date returned: _____

Title: _____

Author: _____

Borrowed from: _____

Loaned to: _____

Date returned: _____

The New York Times

April 3, 1878

THE EFFECTS OF READING BOYS' STORIES

Last evening two boys named Walter Montgomery and James Daley were taken to the Central Office by Sergeant Warts, of the Fourteenth Precinct. They had applied to him for food and means to return to their homes at Providence, R.I. They had been excited by novel-reading, and ran away from home to go West, where they expected to become trappers. When they reached New York their funds gave out and their ambition fled.

Title:

Author:

Borrowed from:

Loaned to:

Date returned:

Title:

Author:

Borrowed from:

Loaned to:

Date returned:

Title: _____

Author: _____

Borrowed from: _____

Loaned to: _____

Date returned: _____

Title: _____

Author: _____

Borrowed from: _____

Loaned to: _____

Date returned: _____

Title:

Author:

Borrowed from:

Loaned to:

Date returned:

Title:

Author:

Borrowed from:

Loaned to:

Date returned:

Title: _____

Author: _____

Borrowed from: _____

Loaned to: _____

Date returned: _____

Title: _____

Author: _____

Borrowed from: _____

Loaned to: _____

Date returned: _____

Title: _____

Author: _____

Borrowed from: _____

Loaned to: _____

Date returned: _____

Title: _____

Author: _____

Borrowed from: _____

Loaned to: _____

Date returned: _____

The New York Times

April 30, 1859

LITERARY TOPICS
BOOKS, AUTHORS, AND ARTISTS.

Another literary sphinx has appeared among British novelists. The author of *Scenes of Clerical Life,* whose new novel of *Adam Bede* is making a great sensation among novel readers on both sides of the Atlantic, has been generally believed to be a Mr. George Elliott; but this appears to be nothing more than one of those disreputable literary artifices, known as a *nomme de plume,* by which young adventurers in literature shield themselves from the disaster of a failure, until two or three successes give them sufficient courage to come out under their own proper name. . . . As to George Elliott, his real name is asserted by some of the English weekly journals to be Higgins, which is a sufficient apology for his taking any body's name but his own. The *Illustrated Times,* however, which is one of the best written on the London weeklies, says that the author of *Adam Bede* is a woman. It is hardly possible that a book containing so much masculine thought, should be the production of a woman, but then it must be remembered that keen critics once gravely asserted that such a book as *Jane Eyre* could never have been written by one of the gentle sex.

Title:

Author:

Borrowed from:

Loaned to:

Date returned:

Title:

Author:

Borrowed from:

Loaned to:

Date returned:

Title: _____

_____

Author: _____

Borrowed from: _____

Loaned to: _____

Date returned: _____

_____

_____

_____

Title: _____

_____

Author: _____

Borrowed from: _____

Loaned to: _____

Date returned: _____

_____

_____

Title:

Author:

Borrowed from:

Loaned to:

Date returned:

Title:

Author:

Borrowed from:

Loaned to:

Date returned:

𝕿𝖍𝖊 𝕹𝖊𝖜 𝖄𝖔𝖗𝖐 𝕿𝖎𝖒𝖊𝖘

Oct. 5, 1941

THE GENIUS OF VIRGINIA WOOLF

IN HER LAST BOOK THE ENGLISH NOVELIST AGAIN SAYS THE UNSAYABLE

By Hudson Strode

BETWEEN THE ACTS. By Virginia Woolf. 219 pp. New York: Harcourt, Brace & Co. $2.50

When Virginia Woolf quietly wrote a farewell note to her husband, took her stick—so fixed is habit—and went on her favorite walk across the summery meadows down to the Ouse to slip under the water, it was a sad hour for English letters. Why did she do it? No one knows precisely. It may well have been a combination of four factors—sorrow over the war with its breeding hatreds; the demolishment of her Bloomsbury apartment ("They are destroying all the beautiful things!" she cried); the revising of her book, which always caused her pain; and the fear of "an old madness" coming over her.

"Between the Acts" had been completed before her death, but she was still working on the final revisions when the compulsion for the ultimate escape seized her. It is with curiosity, profound regret, and a cool sort of reverence that one takes up the last work of the sole indisputable genius among contemporary British women-of-letters.

As in most of her novels, the cream of "Between the Acts" lies between the lines—in the haunting overtones. And the best of the show—the part one really cares about—happens between the acts and immediately before the pageant begins and just after it is over. So the play is not really the thing at all. It is merely the focal point, the hub of the wheel, the peg on which to hang the bright ribbons and dark chords of the author's supersensitive perceptions and illuminated knowledge.

A B C

page

D E f

G H I

J K L

$S\ T\ U\ V$

page

W X Y Z

The New York Times

Jan. 8, 1900

FINDS FORTUNE IN A BOOK

INDIANAPOLIS, Jan. 7.—John B. Pankey, manager of the English Hotel, at English, Crawford County, while looking through the wareroom of the hotel to-day found a book with the name of Philip McDonnough of Poughkeepsie, N.Y., written on the fly-leaf.

Between the leaves of the book were four $100 bills, one $500 bill, and two $1,000 bills. The book is entitled "Protestantism and Catholicism Compared in Their Efforts on the Civilization of Europe."

Mr. Pankey has no idea how the book came to be in the wareroom of the hotel, nor does he recall ever having a guest by the name of McDonnough at his hotel.

A B C

D E f

page

J K L

page

M N O

S T U V

ꟃ x ꟗ z